W9-BLO-772

Individual Counseling
Lessons for Adolescents
(Grades 7-12)

By Robert P. Bowman, Ph.D.
&
Susan C. Bowman, Ed.S., L.P.C.

YouthLight, Inc.
Post Office Box 115
Chapin, South Carolina 29036
(800) 209-9774 (803) 345-1070
Fax (803) 345-0888
YL@youthlightbooks.com
www.youthlightbooks.com

© 2012, 2007, 2005, 2000, 1998 by
YouthLight, Inc.
Chapin, SC 29036

All rights reserved.
One copy of the Lessons may be made for the express purpose of
providing the material to an adolescent. Other reproductions can not be made
without written permission.

Cover Design by Elizabeth Madden
Illustrations by Walt Lardner
Project Layout by Melissa Hare

ISBN 1-889636-11-8

Library of Congress 98-061125

10 9 8 7 6 5
Printed in the United States of America

This material has been adapted from
Becoming a Co-Pilot: A Handbook for Mentors of Adolescents
by Robert P. Bowman, Ph.D. & Susan C. Bowman, Ed.S., L.P.C. ©1997

Introduction

As a middle or high school counselor you may be faced with many duties such as scheduling, testing, record keeping, coordinating programs or school events, parent/teacher consulting, classroom guidance, etc. Oh, did we forget to mention the line of students outside your door waiting to see you?

Middle and high school counselors have to juggle many different roles and have only a limited amount of time to work directly with students. This book can be a valuable resource during these direct one-to-one meetings with students. It may also be useful in some small group counseling and large group guidance sessions.

How This Book Can Be Useful

In particular, this book may be useful in the following ways:

1. It can be used as a needs assessment tool. Students can look through the topics with you and select one or more on which to begin exploring. In this way, the book helps you and the student to identify a place to start.

2. It can provide a catalyst that can help you and a student approach a topic that might be emotionally sensitive to the student. It may be more comfortable for a student to begin sharing personal information about such a topic if it were introduced through a story, or an activity, rather than through direct questioning.

3. It can be a valuable information resource on a variety of topics that are personalized for adolescent students. It contains specific considerations, strategies, and hints that can help them explore and set new goals for themselves.

4. It can help counseling become more comprehensive and developmental in nature. The fifteen lessons in this book cover a wide range of guidance topics designed to help adolescents increase their coping competencies.

5. It can facilitate a more comfortable and engaging counseling process. By working through the lessons together, you and your student will become partners in the learning process.

Recommendations for Using this Book

On the following pages, there are fifteen lessons each containing information and activities that can be used as discussion starters with your student. Each lesson can help you explore with your student important issues in his/her life and think through various strategies for dealing with them. Each lesson is interactive, thought provoking, encouraging and outcome oriented.

1. Have your student to look through fifteen topics with you. Then, together, select the one(s) that seem most relevant or urgent to deal with first.

2. Work through these lessons together, giving the lead to your student as much as possible. Occasionally stop and make sure he/she understands the concepts. Once you both have read a story or activity, discuss the information together.

3. The 15 lessons contain quotes, realistic stories, checklists, and activities that provide opportunities for you and the student to have discussions on a variety of important issues. We encourage you to be open and honest with your views while accepting your student's own opinions.

4. Use the lessons occasionally, not during every meeting with your student. Remember that the lessons should not become the primary focus of your counseling sessions. They are intended to help the student focus on some important aspects of personal development.

5. Don't worry too much about the sequence in which you cover these lessons with your student. You and your student may change the lesson sequence at any time. Also, don't push to complete every part of each lesson in order. Let your student decide what to cover.

6. Some of these lessons can be covered in one meeting while others may take extra time. Don't hesitate to stop and "capture the opportunity" if the student gets off the topic into something personally relevant.

7. Once your student has worked through some of the lessons, encourage him/her to work with a younger student on the same lesson(s). With your encouragement and guidance, this can be an extremely rewarding experience for the student.

Table of Contents

LESSON 1: PERSONAL STRENGTHS

"Learning about one's personal strengths is an important step toward building the kind of self-confidence and positive motivation that can last a lifetime."

Anonymous

What do you think of when you hear "personal strength?" Many adolescents think of how physically strong they are or how well they can perform in an athletic event or sport. Others may think about how well they are doing in particular subjects in school. However, a person has many more strengths than just athletic and academic abilities.

©YouthLight, Inc.

Mary's Story

Mary was a seventeen year old who was in a special class for adolescents with low IQ scores. She was small for her age and not very athletic. One spring, she was traveling in a small airplane to visit her father who lived in a village in Alaska. An unexpectedly fierce blizzard caused the plane to make a crash landing in the mountains, far from civilization. Both pilots suffered broken legs and the only other passenger besides Mary was knocked unconscious. Fortunately Mary was only slightly hurt.

For the next few days, Mary gathered edible plants and rigged a device that would gather the sun's heat to melt snow for water. She also ripped apart the plane seat and used the material and stuffing to help keep the injured people warm.

Mary was able to keep all three of them alive for more than a week until they were finally discovered by a rescue party. Through Mary's persistence, caring, knowledge of survival strategies, and will to survive, she saved her own life as well as the lives of the others.

Most people in Mary's neighborhood were not aware that she had many strengths. She had never excelled in a sport or in her schoolwork as compared to others her age. However, Mary had several strengths others her age did not have. They included knowledge, skills, and abilities which she used to help herself and her companions survive a life-threatening experience.

Discussion Questions:

1. How do you think Mary gained her personal strengths?

2. Do you believe the following quote? Why or why not? "Everyone is a genius in some way."

3. How can it help someone to learn about his/her personal strengths?

©YouthLight, Inc.

Personal Strength Words

1. Look through the list of "90 Personal Strength Words" on the next page. Write "Me" in front of the words that best describe your personal strengths. Place a "C" in front of any that describe your Counselor's strengths.

2. Discuss how your list of words differs from your Counselor's list. How are they similar?

3. Explore how each of you have used your personal strengths to:
    • Survive an emergency situation.
    • Cope with someone who is not friendly with you.
    • Start working toward a goal that you have been putting off.
    • Finish a project that you are tired of.
    • Bring about a success in school.
    • Bring about a success outside of school.

©YouthLight, Inc.

90 Personal Strength Words

A
___Accepting
___Adventurous
___Appreciative
___Artistic
___Assertive
___Athletic

B
___Bold
___Brave
___Bright

C
___Calm
___Caring
___Cautious
___Clever
___Confident
___Considerate
___Cooperative
___Courageous
___Courteous
___Creative
___Curious

D
___Dedicated
___Dependable
___Determined
___Devoted
___Disciplined

E
___Eager
___Efficient
___Encouraging
___Energetic
___Enthusiastic

F
___Fair
___Faithful

___Flexible
___Forgiving
___Friendly
___Fun-Loving

G
___Generous
___Gentle
___Giving
___Good Sport

H
___Hard Worker
___Helpful
___Honest
___Humble
___Humorous

I
___Independent
___Insightful
___Interested
___Involved

L
___Laidback
___Leader
___Likable
___Loving
___Loyal

M
___Mature
___Motivated

N
___Neat
___Nurturing

O
___On Task
___Open–minded

___Optimistic
___Organized

P
___Patient
___Perceptive
___Persevering
___Positive
___Prepared
___Punctual

Q
___Quiet

R
___Reasonable
___Reliable
___Resourceful
___Respectful

S
___Self-Aware
___Sensitive
___Sharing
___Sincere
___Supportive
___Survivalist

T
___Team Player
___Thoughtful
___Tolerant
___Trustworthy

U
___Understanding
___Unique
___Unselfish

W
___Warm
___Witty

Optional Activities

1. Make a collage using magazine pictures and/or symbols that represent your personal strengths. Hang this in your room as a reminder of those abilities you possess.

2. Find an object that symbolizes your list of "Personal Strength Words." If the object is small enough, carry it around with you as a reminder of your personal strengths.

3. Think of other people you both have known or heard about, that show some of your same personal strengths.

©YouthLight, Inc.

©YouthLight, Inc.

LESSON 2: CHARACTER BUILDING

"Character is like a tree and reputation like its shadow. The shadow is what we think of it; the tree is the real thing."
Abraham Lincoln

Being successful means more than merely having money, power, and other things that show your accomplishments. These things are merely signs that you have achieved something. They do not show what kind of person you are on the inside. Character building is one way to work on your inner self. It focuses on working to improve your beliefs and attitudes about yourself and others.

©YouthLight, Inc.

Charles Lindbergh's Story *

Charles Lindbergh was one of the most famous heroes of the 20th century. He was the first pilot to fly an airplane nonstop across the Atlantic Ocean between the United States and Europe. Lindbergh was a shy, quiet young man when he accomplished this feat. Many people remember him only for this heroic flight. But, Lindbergh was also someone who had many personal difficulties in his life. For example, he and his wife had a baby who was kidnapped and murdered.

In spite of his personal successes and problems, Lindbergh worked throughout his life on his own personal character. That is, he thought about his personality and his beliefs about things and kept working to improve himself. The following is his own description of his character building technique.

Lindbergh's Character Technique *

At night I would read off my list of character factors, and those which I had fulfilled satisfactorily during the day I would mark with a red (X); those I had not been called upon to demonstrate that day would get no mark. But those character factors which I had actually violated each day I would mark with a black (X). I began to check myself from day to day and compare my (marks) from month to month and year to year. I was glad to notice that there was an improvement as I grew older.

Charles Lindbergh

Discussion Questions:

1. How do you think people develop character? Where does it come from?

2. What are some kinds of situations that can affect our character for the better? For worse?

3. What kinds of character do you think helped Charles Lindbergh accomplish his famous flight? (Look through the following "Six Pillars of Character" for ideas.

* From Mosley, (1976), p. 51.

©YouthLight, Inc.

The Six Pillars of Character

Trustworthiness

Respect

Responsibility

Justice & Fairness

Caring

Civic Virtue & Citizenship

©YouthLight, Inc.

Applying the "Six Pillars" to Our Lives

Under each of the following Six Pillars, you will find "Do's" and "Don'ts" that show us how we can apply each of these character traits to our lives. Take one Pillar at a time and explore each example under it. Both you and your counselor should try to think of a time when you or someone you know showed this aspect of the Pillar. Perhaps you can complete a discussion of one Pillar during each of your meetings together.

©YouthLight, Inc.

Showing Character

I. TRUSTWORTHINESS
Worthy of trust, honor, and confidence

Honesty

Do's

☞ Tell the truth, the whole truth, and nothing but the truth.

☞ Be forthright, candid, and frank.

☞ Be sincere—say what you mean, mean what you say.

☞ If you find property, try to return it to its owner.

Don'ts

🛑 Don't betray a trust; strive to meet the legitimate expectations of those who trust you.

🛑 Don't lie (purposely misrepresenting facts or opinions).

🛑 Don't deliberately deceive or mislead by any means (concealing, distorting, telling half-truths).

🛑 Don't be devious or tricky.

🛑 Don't withhold important information in relationships of trust.

🛑 Don't steal another's property.

🛑 Don't cheat, defraud, or engage in tricks or deceptions.

Integrity and Courage

Do's

☞ Stand–up for your beliefs about right and wrong. Be yourself and resist social pressure to do things you think are wrong.

☞ "Walk your talk;" show commitment, courage, and self-discipline by doing the right thing regardless of personal cost.

Pages 9-15 reprinted from *Ethics: Easier Said Than Done*, with permission of the Josephson Institute of Ethics (c) 1992.

©YouthLight, Inc.

Promise-Keeping

Do's

☞ Be reliable, keep your word—pay your debts, return what you borrow.

☞ Make only those commitments that you firmly intend to keep and reasonably think you can keep.

Don'ts

🛑 Don't use tricky, unreasonable, or bad faith interpretations of the language of an agreement to evade commitments.

Fidelity and Loyalty

Do's

☞ Keep confidential information confidential; be discreet with private information that could be embarrassing or harmful to others.

☞ Within the limits of your other ethical obligations, be loyal by standing by, supporting, helping, and protecting your family, friends, teachers, employers, school, community, and country.

Don'ts

🛑 Don't talk behind people's backs, spread rumors, or engage in harmful gossip.

🛑 Don't violate other ethical principles in the name of loyalty—lying, cheating, stealing, or harming others to keep or win a friendship or gain approval.

🛑 Don't betray your loyalty by asking a friend to do something wrong to keep your friendship.

©YouthLight, Inc.

II. RESPECT
Regard for the dignity, worth, and autonomy of all persons (including self)

Do's

☞ Treat all people with respect by being courteous and polite.

☞ Respect the autonomy of others. Taking into account their age and maturity, respect the rights of individuals to make decisions about their own lives.

☞ Be tolerant, appreciative, and accepting of individual differences.

☞ Judge all people on their merits, not on their race, religion, nationality, gender, physical or mental condition, social or economic status, or any other improper factor.

Don'ts

🛑 Don't insult, abuse, demean, mistreat, or harass others.

🛑 Don't make inappropriate or unwanted comments about a person's race, religion, gender, or sexual orientation.

🛑 Don't use, manipulate, exploit, or take advantage of other people.

III. RESPONSIBILITY
Acknowledgement and performance of duties to others and self

Accountability
Do's

☞ Think before you act—consider the possible consequences on yourself and others and decide whether the act is honest, fair, caring, and respectful to all who will be affected.

☞ Be accountable; accept responsibility for the consequences of your actions and inactions.

©YouthLight, Inc.

☞ Be reliable; perform your duties.

☞ Set a good example with your own conduct; act as if someone whose respect you want is always watching.

☞ Take the initiative to make your society, school, or home life better for yourself and others.

Don'ts

🛑 Don't blame others for your mistakes or take credit for the achievements of others.

Pursuit of Excellence

Do's

☞ Do your best; make everything you do worthy of your pride.

☞ Be perseverant; meet your responsibilities even when it is difficult to do.

IV. JUSTICE & FAIRNESS

Making decisions that are just and fair.

Do's

☞ Treat all people fairly.

☞ Be open-minded, listen to others, and try to understand what they are saying and feeling.

☞ In making decisions, fairly consider all relevant information, including opposing viewpoints.

☞ Make decisions with impartiality based on consistent and appropriate standards.

©YouthLight, Inc.

Don'ts

🛑 Don't take unfair advantage of the mistakes or ignorance of others.

🛑 Don't take more than your fair share.

🛑 Don't let personal feelings interfere with decisions that should be made objectively.

V. CARING
Regard for the well-being of others

Do's

☞ Show that you care about others through kindness, caring, generosity, sharing, and compassion.

☞ Live by the Golden Rule—treat others the way you want them to treat you.

Don'ts

🛑 Don't be selfish, mean, cruel, or insensitive to the feelings of others.

VI. CIVIC VIRTUE & CITIZENSHIP
Recognition of and living up to social obligations

Do's

☞ Obey laws and school rules.

☞ Do your share; stay informed; vote; protect your family and community; and report crimes.

☞ Be charitable and altruistic.

©YouthLight, Inc.

Optional Activity

Use the Lindbergh method of character building. Make several photocopies of the "Six Pillars of Character" (see pages 9-15) and punch holes in them so they can be clipped in a three ring binder. Each day (or week), use one color pen (or marker) to check off which items you fulfilled. Use a different color to indicate those which you violated or make two lists each day, one of any character traits you fulfilled, the other of any traits you violated. Periodically, look back to see if you have made an improvement over time.

©YouthLight, Inc.

LESSON 3: GOAL SETTING

*"Dreams are airplanes that are in the sky.
Goals are the engines that
can make them fly."*

R. P. Bowman

Unfortunately, many young people don't think very often about setting positive and realistic goals for themselves. The most successful people know how to set an achievable, positive goal and then take action that will bring about goal attainment.

It has been said that "If you don't know where you are going, you will never get there." Unless you know how to make achievable plans for yourself, you will not find much success in your life.

©YouthLight, Inc.

Carl Lewis' Story *

Carl Lewis has set several world records and won numerous Olympic gold medals in track and field events. These remarkable achievements did not come easy for him. Growing up, Carl felt like the runt of the family and did not seem to have an aptitude for any sport. When young people in his neighborhood established teams for different sports, Carl was often the last one picked.

Despite his small size, Carl did not stop pursuing his dream of becoming a winning athlete. He wanted to find something he could do better than his sister. So he worked hard practicing for track events. He set his sights on one competition at a time and finally won the long jump competition in a regional Jesse Owens meet. Later, he continued to achieve one success after another until he became one of the most famous athletes in the world. Carl Lewis started with a dream, then worked hard to achieve one goal at a time until he finally reached and surpassed it.

For example, Carl used this technique of setting and achieving small goals when attempting a long jump. Just before a jump, he carefully planned each of his steps as a separate goal. Then he pictured in his mind his ultimate leap into the air. The results speak for themselves. In 1981, Carl broke the indoor long jump world record. In 1983, he became the first athlete in nearly a century to win three events in the national championships. In 1984, he won four gold medals in the Olympics and was named "Male Athlete of the Year" by the Associated Press two years in a row. Since then, Carl Lewis has won even more world championship events. In 1996, he was the second athlete to ever win gold medals in the same event (the long jump) in four Olympics.

Discussion Questions:

1. What is the importance of having a positive dream for your future? What are some of your dreams for your future?

2. What do you think are the main reasons people do not achieve their goals?

3. What can you learn from Carl Lewis' story that might help you?

* Adapted from Klots (1995) except for information about his 1996 Olympic achievement.

©YouthLight, Inc.

Long and Short-Term Goals

You may have a dream that seems impossible for you to ever reach. Instead of becoming discouraged, try to focus on what your first step might be. Next, try to accomplish that first step to the best of your abilities. Then, plan other steps you will need to take and accomplish them one at a time. Each of these steps is called a short-term goal. Remember, a mountain can only be climbed one step at a time.

Long-Term Goals

Your dream is an accomplishment called a long-term goal. It may take you a long time before you finally reach it. What is a goal that you would like to accomplish:

• Within the next year? _____

• Within the next ten years? _____

• Within your lifetime? _____

Short-Term Goals

Once you have developed some long–term goals, pick one to focus on first and plan the steps you will need to reach it. Then you will work to complete these steps, one at a time. Each of these steps is called a "short-term goal." Choose one of the long-term goals you listed above and write it on the first line below. Then, list the steps or short–term goals you will need to reach on your way to achieving your long–term goal.

Long-Term Goal:

    Step 1: _____

    Step 2: _____

    Step 3: _____

    Other Steps? _____

_____

©YouthLight, Inc.

More Challenging Goals

When planning a challenging goal, you may not be able to determine all the steps that you must take to achieve it. It is usually better to take more time to explore what makes it so challenging. Then, determine your first step and commit to a start date. One of the most difficult things to do in working toward a challenging goal is to take the first step.

Using the following three procedures, determine a goal and a first step, then commit to where and when you will take this first step.

1. On a separate piece of paper, write or draw something academically or personally that you would like to improve. (Some people express much more in a drawing.)

2. Decide on a "first step" you could take toward making the improvement. Write or draw yourself doing this step.

3. Commit to a day and time that you will take this "first step." Write this commitment in a goal statement. For example, "At 4:30 today, I will start my social studies homework."

Optional Activities

1. Talk about times each of you succeeded in reaching your goals.
   A. A success you remember having as a child.
   B. A success you have had more recently.
   C. A success you hope to have in the future.
   Also discuss what is a success and what is a failure. Note that a failure to one might be a success to another person, and vice versa.

2. Keep a "Success Journal," which is a diary-like booklet in which you will write about your successes as you achieve them. You could include a list of some of your greatest successes in a student Portfolio. Some things that might be included are:
   A. "A brief description of a success and what I did that helped me to succeed (try to use some of your own personal strength words)."
   B. "Something I learned about myself from this success."
   C. "How this successful experience felt to me."

©YouthLight, Inc.

LESSON 4: STUDY HABITS AND SKILLS

"Skill and confidence are an unconquered army."

George Herbert

If you would like to improve your grades in school, there are some tricks you can learn that will help you. These tricks are called "study habits and skills." Getting better grades may depend more on how well you use these skills than on how much time you spend studying.

© YouthLight, Inc.

James' Story

For years, James wished he could improve his school grades. Each time he received his report card, he was disappointed, but not surprised. His mother would say, "James, you have to study harder!" and James would start off each new grading period by doing just that. He studied very hard and did well for about two weeks. Then, he started putting off doing his homework and his grades started to slide once again. He became tired of trying so hard, and he began to watch more television and go out with his friends more often. Soon, he was failing many of his classes, and James became even more discouraged. Finally, James gave up trying because he didn't believe there was much hope.

This cycle is an easy one for students to slip into. Once you find yourself behind in your school work or become tired of trying so hard, it is easy to begin putting things off. It has been said that the difference between one letter grade and the one above it (for example the difference between a "C" and "B") only requires 5% more work. Why then do some students seem to get good grades while working so little to achieve them? One advantage they have is their confidence level. Other advantages are their study habits and skills.

Discussion Questions:

1. What are some reasons students your age put off doing schoolwork?

2. When have you ever felt like James? What did you do about it?

3. If you ever decide to encourage a younger student to study harder, how would you do it?

©YouthLight, Inc.

Keys to Becoming a Confident Learner

The following are strategies some students have used to become more confident about their abilities to succeed in school.

Key #1: **Set a few new goals at a time.** Review the previous lesson on goal setting.

Key #2: **See yourself being successful.** Picture in your mind what it will be like when you succeed at each of your goals. Remember to think of this picture whenever you begin to feel frustrated or discouraged.

Key #3: **Control your inner voice.** We all occasionally talk to ourselves in our minds. Unfortunately, some of the things we say to ourselves discourage us and make us want to put off or quit working so hard at something we need to do. Change these negative messages to more positive ones like the following:

Negative Self-Messages	**Positive Self-Messages**
• "I just can't do this work."	• "I can do this work."
• "I will never be able to do this."	• "I will be able to do this."
• "I will never be good at this."	• "I can keep improving."
• "I know I'm going to fail this."	• "I'm going to do my best."

Key #4: **Reward your accomplishments.** Once you have accomplished a short-term goal, give yourself a reward. Treat yourself to something special.

Key #5: **Encourage others.** Do you know someone who has become discouraged about school? When this happens, listen to his/her feelings. Then, offer some positive suggestions such as how he/she might find a tutor. When you help others to think more positively, it can have a positive effect on you, too.

©YouthLight, Inc.

30 Study Habits and Skills

Here is a list for you to look through and discuss with your counselor. Begin by rating yourself on each of the items according to how well you use the strategy:

1 = Poor   *3* = So-So   *4* = Good
2 = Not so good   *5* = Excellent

Classroom Effectiveness

_____**1. Keep Good Attendance:** Being in class is perhaps the most important thing you can do for your grades. When you miss a class, it usually takes twice the time to make up your work.

_____**2. Set High Goals:** Write down what grades you hope to accomplish for each class and "aim high."

_____**3. Show a Winning Attitude:** An important part of succeeding in a class is making sure your teacher sees that you care. Participate in class and avoid distractions.

_____**4. Listen Carefully**: Pay close attention to the teacher. Sometimes, you can discover important hints about what to study by listening for emphasis in the teacher's voice.

_____**5. Take Good Notes:** Take brief notes and emphasize the important points by underlining, highlighting, or using creative abbreviations.

© YouthLight, Inc.

Studying Reading Material

____**6. Use "SQ3R":** Survey, Question, Read, Review, and Recite. This is an old, but effective way to study reading material.

____**7. Skim the Chapter Questions First:** This will give you a feel for what is most important in the Chapter. Then look for answers to the questions as you read the Chapter more carefully.

Memorizing Facts

____**8. Use Acronyms:** Take the first letter of each term you want to memorize. Then make a nonsense word out of it. Or, you could create a new sentence with the same first letters for each word. For example, to memorize our solar system's planets in sequence from the sun, you can use the following statement: "My Very Excellent Mother Just Sat Upon Nine Pins." Another version for older students is, "Mary's Violet Eyes Made John Sit Up Nights Pondering" (Mercury, Venus, Earth, Mars, Jupiter, Saturn, Uranus, Neptune, and Pluto).

____**9. Use Word Associations:** Memorize a list of words that rhyme with each number 1-10. For example, one/run, two/shoe, three/tree, four/door, five/hive, six/sticks, seven/heaven, eight-/skate, nine/sign, and ten/hen. Then in sequence, picture each item you are trying to memorize with one of the rhyming terms.

____**10. Use "Rap":** Recite the terms or words you are trying to memorize with a rap rhythm. Rhythm can help you memorize much faster.

Writing a Term Paper or Project

____**11. Research:** Take the time to study your topic before you begin writing. Take brief notes and make sure you cite each source. This will help you relocate the information later if you need it.

____**12. Outline:** The key to an organized paper is a logical, clearly written outline.

©YouthLight, Inc.

____**13. Draft:** Don't worry about perfection here, just "get the words out." For example, it is sometimes better to avoid writing a paper in the order that it will finally appear. Start by writing the section that will be easiest for you.

____**14. Recast:** Once the first draft is completed, rework each section repeatedly.

____**15. Polish:** Check carefully the flow of what you have written and rewrite as needed for clarity.

____**16. Proofread:** Always double check your paper. Then have someone else double check it, especially for errors.

Taking a Test

____**17. Prepare:** Make sure you have enough time to study for a test. Sometimes it may help to have a study partner or team. Also, make sure you have enough sleep and eat a healthy breakfast before the test.

____**18. Reduce Stress:** Think of the test as a challenge and not a threat. If you are worried slow down; take a few slow, deep breaths; and make positive statements to yourself about how you are capable of succeeding on the test.

____**19. Become Motivated:** Remember that each test is important and don't give up. Give each question your best effort.

____**20. Be Test-Wise:** Make educated guesses and watch your pacing.

Studying Effectively at Home

____**21. Use your time wisely:** Don't spend too much time on one subject. When attempting to memorize, it is usually better to study in short 20 - 30 minute intervals with a brief break, than try to study for an hour or two, straight through. Perhaps, play "Beat the Clock" by guessing how long it will take you to complete the work you have in one subject. Then, time yourself and try to complete the work before that time elapses.

____**22. Set Goals:** Set a goal each day before you begin working on your homework.

©YouthLight, Inc.

23. Prioritize: Decide which assignment is most important and do it first.

24. Prevent Distractions: You will accomplish more in less time if you do not have a television, stereo, or busy phone nearby. Find a place to study that is quiet, and comfortable. Some students, however, study better with soft music playing in the background.

25. Use Study Tools: Use your creativity to develop ways to use study tools Attaching notes to your bedroom wall or using homemade flash cards can be helpful. Some students have used a cassette tape-recorder to playback key things to remember.

Using Resource People

26. Ask Your Teacher: Don't be afraid to ask your teacher for assistance. It shows you care.

27. Ask Other School Staff: There are several other people in your school who may help you if you ask.

28. Ask Other Students: Other students may be very willing to help you or work with you. Perhaps you can find a "study partner" or study group.

29. Ask Your Family: Don't forget that others in your family can be great resources.

30. Ask Other People: There may be other people in your community that would be pleased to help you. Some communities have tutoring services, phone-in homework help lines, and other student assistance programs available.

©YouthLight, Inc.

Follow-Up

Look over any of the previous items that you marked "4" or "5" and recognize your strong points. Then, look at the items you marked "1" or "2" and set goals to improve in these areas. Select a strategy you will begin working on with your counselor. Remember, "Your study skills are your school survival skills. . .use them wisely."

Optional Activity

Develop a weekly calendar showing your subject areas, assignments, tests, and short-term goals. Perhaps you can provide yourself with a reward each time you accomplish a goal.

©YouthLight, Inc.

LESSON 5: CAREER EXPLORATION

"Find out what you like doing best and get someone to pay you for doing it."
Katherine Whitehorn

Every teenager should start thinking about different possible careers. There are several factors that will influence your career decisions. Unfortunately, some people may try to discourage teens from believing they can reach their career dreams. Usually this is because the teenager's goals may seem unrealistic. But, don't lose sight of your dreams. There may be some goals that would be difficult for you to reach. But, if you have enough determination and are willing to make the necessary sacrifices and investments, you just might reach your dream career. On the next page is a list of some famous people who became very successful because of their determination and hard work.

© YouthLight, Inc.

Nine People Who Refused to be Discouraged

Thomas Edison was told by his teachers that he was too "stupid" to learn anything. Later, he repeatedly made more than 3,000 mistakes on his way to inventing the light bulb. Eventually he held 1,093 patents.

Wilma Randolph contracted polio and scarlet fever as a child and wore leg braces for nine years. She eventually became the first woman from the United States to win three Olympic gold medals in track and field.

Albert Einstein was four years old before he could speak and seven before he could read. One of his teachers described him as mentally slow, unsociable, and "adrift." He was later expelled from school. He is still considered to be one of the greatest physicists of all time.

Walt Disney was fired by a newspaper editor when he was young. He was told that he had "no creative ideas." His company's parks, movies, and other products touch the hearts of millions of people each year.

Michael Jordan was cut from his high school basketball team. Later, his accomplishments inspired several prominent sports writers to declare him the best pro-basketball player ever.

Oprah Winfrey suffered many drawbacks as a child because she was emotionally and physically abused. Yet, she became the first African American woman to host a nationally syndicated weekday talk show and to own her own television and film distribution company.

Bill Cosby became discouraged and dropped out of high school. He later received his doctorate degree in education and became one of the most successful entertainers and businessmen in the world.

Jim Carey also was a discouraged teenager. He dropped out of school in the ninth grade. His family was so poor they had to live in a camper and a tent. Later, he became the first comedian to earn twenty million dollars for appearing in a single film.

Agatha Christie had a writing disability so severe that she had to dictate her stories for others to type. Yet, she became one of the most famous writers of mystery novels.

©YouthLight, Inc.

What's Important to You?

The following are some of the reasons why people choose and enjoy certain careers over others. Select the three items that are the most important to you.

❑ Working with others in a team

❑ Working alone

❑ Working outdoors

❑ Being my own boss

❑ Receiving longer vacations

❑ Having flexible work hours

❑ Fixing or repairing things

❑ Creating or developing new things

❑ Working with computers

❑ Working at a job requiring physical strength

❑ Helping people or animals

❑ Playing a sport

❑ Entertaining others

❑ Traveling

❑ Selling things

❑ Helping people solve their problems

❑ Playing a musical instrument or singing

❑ Building things

© YouthLight, Inc.

10 Job Skills Employers Want to See

The following is a list of job skills that employers look for in new employees. Discuss how each of these "job skills" could be applied to different careers.

1. **Interpersonal Skills:** Be able to get along well with others.

2. **Reliability:** Show that you are a dependable person.

3. **Honesty:** Be trustworthy.

4. **Work Habits:** Be consistently responsible.

5. **Communication Skills:** Be able to write and speak effectively.

6. **Application Abilities:** Be able to apply knowledge to practical situations.

7. **Positive Attitude:** Be optimistic toward your job and employer.

8. **Persistence:** Be able to keep your efforts going.

9. **Flexible:** Be able to shift tasks easily.

10. **Resourceful:** Know when and where to find answers or ask for assistance.

©YouthLight, Inc.

Careers in My Family

Write the name of each of the following members of your family. Then list and tell about the type of job or career in which they have worked. Then, using the "10 Job Skills" on the previous page, write the numbers of the skills (1-10) that you think are the most important for each particular job. If you don't know the careers of some of these people, leave the space blank.

Mother: _____

Father: _____

Step-Parent or Guardian: _____

Grandparents: _____

Older Brothers or Sisters: _____

Aunts and Uncles: _____

Other Family Members: _____

Follow Up

1. Are you interested in one or more of the above listed careers? if so, which one(s)?

   _____

2. If you don't have a special interest in your family's careers, write one or more careers that are interesting to you. Then, write the numbers of the skills that you think are most important for that career.

   _____

3. Interview your counselor? What are the skills most important for his/her job?

   _____

©YouthLight, Inc.

Optional Activities

1. Choose at least two careers that interest you the most. Add one or two careers that you are somewhat interested in. Then, go to the media center, career center, or guidance office and look up descriptions of those careers.

2. Find and interview one or more people who work in each of the careers you identified in #1.

3. Check with the vocational program that is affiliated with your school. See if there is a "Job Shadow" type program and volunteer to become involved in it. Perhaps your counselor can assist you with this.

© YouthLight, Inc.

LESSON 6: FAMILY

Family is "The we of me."
Carson McCullers

The word "family" is difficult to define. Some people think of a family as a group of people who are related to one another. Others view it as a group of people who are living together in the same home. Regardless of how you define family, it is a group of people who have a powerful influence on the life of each of its members.

Every family has its wonderful points and its difficulties. There are no families that are perfect and problem-free. Likewise, there are no families that are all bad.

©YouthLight, Inc.

Jose's Story

Jose was a friendly boy who was doing well in school. Others believed that he was very fortunate to have such a "good" family which didn't seem to have many problems. Some of the other students in his school were jealous of him, believing that he had it "so easy" in his life. But, these students didn't realize how difficult Jose's life was with his family.

One day, Jose came to school very quiet. Other people didn't notice much, but Jose didn't talk to anyone that day. A few students thought Jose was being rude and unfriendly when he didn't talk to them. Later, another boy thought Jose was staring at him and it made him very uncomfortable. He walked over and threatened Jose that he would make him sorry if didn't stop. Jose threw his books on the floor and left school.

The next day, another student found out that Jose's younger brother had runaway from home earlier in the week. In addition, his favorite uncle died about the same time.

Discussion Questions:

1. What do you think is the reason that Jose didn't tell anyone about what was happening in his family?

2. Why do some students have difficulty requesting help for their family problems?

3. What do you think are the most common problems that most families have?

4. What are the main reasons that a family is so important to each of its members?

©YouthLight, Inc.

My Family

Circle the number after each characteristic below that best describes how you and your family relate with one another.

1 = Almost never   *3* = Unsure   *4* = Some of the time
2 = Seldom   *5* = Almost always

Have fun together.	*1*	*2*	*3*	*4*	*5*
Help each other when there's a problem.	*1*	*2*	*3*	*4*	*5*
Communicate honestly and openly.	*1*	*2*	*3*	*4*	*5*
Make decisions that are fair to one another.	*1*	*2*	*3*	*4*	*5*
Understand each other.	*1*	*2*	*3*	*4*	*5*
Talk positively about each other.	*1*	*2*	*3*	*4*	*5*
Tell your true feelings to each other.	*1*	*2*	*3*	*4*	*5*
Spend enough time together.	*1*	*2*	*3*	*4*	*5*

Follow Up

If you answered most of these items with "1" or "2" it is possible that your family situation may also be having a negative effect on your school work and on your relationships with others. You may want to see someone else who understands and can offer support such as a special friend, another relative or your school counselor.

©YouthLight, Inc.

Family Influence

We are all influenced by our families. Whether we like it or not, the way we think, believe, act, and react are all affected by our families. Sometimes we may be surprised to discover that we act just like someone else in our family. What are some things you learned from your family that you will try to pass on to your own family someday?

Check the items below.

- ❑ Honesty
- ❑ Trustworthiness
- ❑ Patience
- ❑ Humor
- ❑ Pride
- ❑ Generosity
- ❑ Humbleness
- ❑ Good communication
- ❑ Positive attitude
- ❑ Belief in hard work
- ❑ Organization
- ❑ Fairness
- ❑ Friendliness
- ❑ Determination
- ❑ Kindness
- ❑ Respect
- ❑ Religion
- ❑ Appreciation for education
- ❑ Other

Optional Activity

On a large piece of paper, draw your family tree. Include both the mother's and father's sides of the family. Be sure to also include brothers/sisters, adoptive or step-parents, foster parents, guardians, and any other people living in your household. Don't worry if your "tree" ends up looking more like a bush because of all the current family members.

Once the family tree is as complete as you can make it, share with your counselor which people listed in your tree influence you the most in the items listed above.

©YouthLight, Inc.

LESSON 7: HEALTHY RELATIONSHIPS

"(A friend is) a present you give yourself."
Robert Louis Stevenson

Having different kinds of relationships with others provides you with many learning opportunities. Whenever you enter into new relationships, you will learn many new things about yourself and others. This learning process is important in preparing you for adulthood. But, some teenagers seem to keep finding themselves caught in relationships with controlling or abusive people. They may regret ever getting into these unhealthy relationships, yet they keep finding themselves back in them over and over again. Melissa is one of these people.

©YouthLight, Inc.

Melissa's Story

Melissa cannot understand why she always seems to find herself in relationships with guys who are very possessive and controlling. Looking back at the boyfriends she's had, each was very jealous and mean to her.

Melissa does not look for this kind of guy, yet she seems to be more attracted to those who criticize her. As each relationship becomes more negative, Melissa works very hard to save it. But this never seems to work very well.

Melissa's friends told her she needed to find a guy who would treat her with more respect. But Melissa would answer, "The ones that are nice and polite are so boring."

Now, Melissa is dating a guy who will not allow her to spend time alone with her friends. He tells her that where he goes, she goes. Every now and then Melissa sneaks some time with her friends, but she is worried he will find out. Although she is not happy in this relationship, Melissa says she can't tell her boyfriend about her real feelings or he will surely break up with her.

Discussion Questions:

Melissa is an example of someone who repeatedly finds herself in the same kind of unhealthy relationship. Discuss your answers to the following questions:

1. What is unhealthy about this relationship?
2. Why do you think Melissa finds herself attracted to this type of guy?
3. What could Melissa do differently to prevent herself from being in this kind of relationship?
4. In your own relationship(s) with others, how can you reduce the risks of:

- Being with someone too possessive or controlling?

- Being too dependent on the other person?

- Being with someone who will be a negative influence on you?

- Pregnancy?

- Sexually-transmitted diseases?

- Being deeply hurt?

©YouthLight, Inc.

Unhealthy Relationships

The following list contains characteristics of unhealthy relationships. Check those items that apply to one or more of your relationships or to relationships between other people you know.

- ❏ Dominating/Controlling
- ❏ Dishonesty
- ❏ Rushed intimacy
- ❏ Poor communication
- ❏ One-sided attraction
- ❏ Big differences between the people
- ❏ Arguing too frequently
- ❏ Physical abuse
- ❏ Emotional abuse
- ❏ Use of alcohol and/or other drugs
- ❏ Interference by family or friends
- ❏ Flirting with others
- ❏ Rescuer (When one person keeps seeking troubled partners to "help")
- ❏ Troubled companions (When both partners have problems and their relationship is built on trying to rescue each other)

© YouthLight, Inc.

Developing a Healthy Relationship

Here are some ways to increase the chances of getting into a healthy relationship with someone. Discuss each with your counselor.

☞ Start the relationship slowly by having fun and getting to know each other. Talk with each other about your interests, strengths, goals, families, hopes, and fears.

☞ Plan to do a variety of activities together that could decrease the chances of being placed in an uncomfortable situation.

☞ Communicate your feelings openly about what you are and are not looking for in a relationship.

☞ Take turns sharing your personal beliefs and values.

☞ Don't be too pushy or too weak. Stand up for your rights, but don't become over critical of the other person.

☞ It has been said that the key to a healthy relationship is for each person to consistently show four characteristics: caring, accepting, understanding, and trustworthiness.

☞ If you have already experienced several unhealthy relationships or continue to be attracted to the same kinds of troubled people, see a counselor. Through counseling you may be able to discover how you can find happier and healthier relationships.

©YouthLight, Inc.

What do You Look For?

The following list of qualities are what some people your age look for in a relationship. Score each of the following items according to how important it is to you when you are considering a relationship. Discuss your responses with your counselor.

1 = Unimportant   2 = A little important   3 = Very important

___ Good looking

___ A nice car

___ Well dressed

___ Popular

___ Wealthy

___ Humorous

___ Respectful

___ Quiet or shy

___ Career minded

___ Honest

___ Muscular

___ Intelligent

___ Reliable

___ Sexually experienced

___ Sexually abstinent

___ Religious

___ Athletic

___ A close friend

___ Responsible

___ Interested in similar things

___ Outspoken

___ Good listener

___ Older than me

___ Younger than me

___ Adventurous

___ (Other)

©YouthLight, Inc.

Optional Activities

1. Think about a healthy relationship between two people that you've known. Discuss what they did that helped their relationship succeed? Then, think about an unhealthy relationship you have seen. Discuss what hurt their relationship?

2. Interview your school counselor or pastor, and ask what he/she believes are qualities of a healthy relationship.

©YouthLight, Inc.

LESSON 8: PEER PRESSURE

"Learn to navigate your own course.."
Anonymous

Being accepted by peers is very important to most young people. This need for acceptance comes from a basic human need to feel like you belong to some kind of group. Sometimes, to become part of a group, we feel that we should dress like them and do things like them. This may be okay in some groups. However, the need to belong can also influence a teenager to do dangerous, illegal, and/or other negative things.

It would be best if every person your age would carefully select only positive and encouraging friends who avoid getting into trouble. However, this is not the "real world." Consider what happened to Mark in the following story.

©YouthLight, Inc.

Mark's Story

Mark was a new student at school. At the end of his first week, some other students approached him and were very friendly. Later, they asked if he wanted to hang out with them that evening.

Mark wanted to be liked by other students, so he agreed without hesitation. They met in front of the local movie theater and stood there for an hour. Then, one of the boys' brothers picked them up in his car and took them to someone's home. As they entered the house, one of the boys said, "Let's party! My parents are gone for the weekend."

The older brother brought in a case of beer and each of the boys grabbed a can, including Mark. Although Mark was uncomfortable with the situation, he didn't want to be different from the others. Later that evening, the boys were shocked when the parents walked through the door and caught them drinking. It was Mark's first week in the new school and already, he was in trouble.

Discussion Questions:

1. What were some of the risks involved in this particular group of friends?

2. How could Mark have avoided getting into trouble?

3. What else could Mark have done to find friends?

4. When have you felt pressured to do something negative with others your age?

©YouthLight, Inc.

Negative Peer Pressure

Check the things below that you have felt pressure from your peers to do.

❑ Cut classes

❑ Skip school

❑ Smoke cigarettes

❑ Use alcohol

❑ Use other drugs

❑ Steal

❑ Damage or destroy property

❑ Have sex

❑ Sneak out of your home

❑ Run away

❑ Cheat on school work

❑ Act up in class

❑ Be dishonest about something you did

❑ Fight

❑ Pick on someone

❑ Get revenge against someone

❑ Join a gang

❑ Be prejudiced

❑ Say you like something that you don't

❑ Be different from who you really are

❑ Do something daring to "prove" yourself

©YouthLight, Inc.

Positive Peer Pressure

People can also pressure someone to do positive things in his/her life. For example, check the following positive things below that you have felt pressured to do, or tried to get others to do.

❏ Try out for a sport

❏ Improve your appearance

❏ Avoid peers who are bad influences

❏ Change a bad decision into a better one

❏ Be honest about something you did

❏ Join a club or organization

❏ Listen to a different kind of music

❏ Stay out of trouble at school

❏ Try something new that is positive

❏ Do better with your schoolwork

❏ Avoid smoking cigarettes

❏ Avoid drinking alcohol

❏ Avoid drinking and driving

❏ Avoid using illegal drugs

❏ Start a musical group

❏ Abstain from sex

❏ Stay in school

❏ Help someone

❏ Make career choices

❏ Be yourself

❏ Avoid being prejudiced

©YouthLight, Inc.

Optional Activity

Circle of Friends: On a sheet of paper, draw a diagram similar to the one that appears below. This is your "Circle of Friends."

In the circle nearest to "ME," write the names of your closest friends. In the next circle, write names of other people who are friends, but are less close. Then, in the outer circle, write some names of people who you know, but you don't "hang out" with.

Discuss how you would avoid negative pressure if it came from any of the different people in your diagram. Then, talk about how you might use positive peer pressure to help some of these people if they were heading for trouble.

©YouthLight, Inc.

©YouthLight, Inc.

LESSON 9: STRESS

"If you don't learn to control your stress well, it will eventually control you."
Anonymous

Stress is mental tension that causes several physical reactions. When we feel stress from fear, anger, or other feelings, our bodies prepare for "fight or flight." This means that we prepare to confront or get away from what is causing us to be upset. Our bodies do this by increasing our heart rate, blood pressure, breathing, and other physical responses. Once we deal with what is causing the stress, then these physical reactions slow down and we can relax again. However, if we can't or don't take care of the cause of our stress, then we remain tense.

When held for too long, stress can cause us to develop serious physical illnesses. For example, long-held tension is known to be one of the causes of ulcers, hypertension, asthma, hives, depression, and other illnesses. Long-term stress can also cause people to lose their abilities to think clearly and make good decisions. They may become depressed and need help from a professional doctor, psychologist, or counselor.

©YouthLight, Inc.

Tina's Story

Tina was a very hard working senior in high school. Each year she had taken the most difficult classes and received all A's on her report cards. She always expected herself to do better than other students. As a result, Tina didn't take time for friends. During her evenings and weekends and even during lunch, she would find a quiet place to study.

In the spring of her senior year, Tina was diagnosed with mononucleosis (Mono) and had to miss several weeks of school. Though she tried to do her schoolwork at home, she was not able to keep up with all the assignments in one of her subjects. As a result, Tina's situation became increasingly stressful to her. Near the end of the semester, Tina found that her grades had dropped. She felt that her situation had finally become hopeless. To everyone's surprise, she took an overdose of pills, attempting to commit suicide. Fortunately, she did not die.

When she was released from the hospital, Tina started meeting with a counselor. She discovered that she needed to work on how she could feel better about herself and better handle the stress in her life.

Discussion Questions:

1. Was there ever a time when you felt discouraged like Tina? How did you deal with it?

2. What are some positive things Tina could have done instead of trying to hurt herself?

3. What could you do if you noticed a student like Tina in your school?

©YouthLight, Inc.

Stress Test

In learning to handle your stress, it is important to check out how much tension you have at any given time. The following "Stress Test" will help you determine how much stress you are experiencing now. Check each of the following situations that are causing you stress in your life.

- ❏ Death of a relative or friend
- ❏ Pregnancy
- ❏ Troubles with rules or laws
- ❏ Dropping out of school
- ❏ Moved to a new home
- ❏ Fears about your future
- ❏ High expectations of yourself
- ❏ Disappointing grades
- ❏ Feeling pressured to succeed
- ❏ Feeling unsafe at school
- ❏ Boyfriend/girlfriend situations
- ❏ Relative or friend moved away

- ❏ Feeling unsafe outside of school
- ❏ Your friends or lack of them
- ❏ Upset at others your age
- ❏ Transportation difficulties
- ❏ Fears about your health
- ❏ Financial trouble
- ❏ Family problems
- ❏ Loss of a pet
- ❏ New job
- ❏ Leaving home
- ❏ Other problems

Just looking at the number of items you checked is not a good indicator of how much stress you have. Experiencing even a few of these situations could be the cause of a great amount of stress. Look through the items you checked and circle any that you believe are causing you the greatest amount of stress. Once you've finished, talk with your counselor about how much stress you have. Then, continue to the next page to explore ways of coping with your stress.

© YouthLight, Inc.

Learning to Cope With Stress

When we experience a lot of stress in our lives, we must find positive ways to cope with it. People seem to get themselves in the most troublesome situations when they use unhealthy ways of coping with their stress. Learning to cope in healthy ways with stress is one key to success in life.

The following list describes healthy and unhealthy ways of coping with stress. Put checks next to the approaches that best fit your style of coping. Then, discuss the long-term effects of each approach you checked.

Healthy Coping

❑ Writing out a positive step-by-step plan
❑ Taking care of your health
❑ Doing something helpful for someone else
❑ Talking about it with a friend, or family member
❑ Going to a counselor or other professional helper
❑ Doing something active
❑ Taking time to relax
❑ Using humor
❑ Directing your attention to something constructive
❑ Using your faith (for example, praying)
❑ Playing a musical instrument

Unhealthy Coping

❑ Eating too much (or too little)
❑ Taking it out on someone (or something) else
❑ Refusing to talk about it with others
❑ Avoiding (running away or escaping)
❑ Oversleeping
❑ Using alcohol/drugs
❑ Smoking
❑ Making excuses
❑ Denying a problem exists
❑ Hurting yourself physically
   (or thinking about it)

©YouthLight, Inc.

Using Self-Talk

When you are under a lot of stress, it may help to say something to yourself that will calm you down a little. The following are some self-talk statements that can help.

- ➪ "I will learn from this situation and will be a better person because of it."

- ➪ "I know someone who will listen to me and understand my feelings."

- ➪ "Don't sweat the small stuff. . . and this is small stuff, really."

- ➪ "There are no failures, only different degrees of success."

- ➪ "In the long run, is this going to be really important?"

- ➪ "This situation is not a problem, it is an opportunity."

- ➪ "This situation is not a difficulty, it is a challenge."

- ➪ "I can remain calm with this difficult person."

- ➪ "No matter what happens, I will be okay."

- ➪ "I can bear anything for awhile."

- ➪ "I am a worthwhile person!"

- ➪ "I am doing the best I can."

- ➪ "This, too, shall pass."

- ➪ "I am true to myself."

- ➪ "One step at a time."

© YouthLight, Inc.

Optional Activities

1. Start with a deflated balloon. This is like a day without much stress. Describe little events that can cause stress to build such as oversleeping, forgetting about a test, and being accused of something you didn't do. After each story, blow more air into the balloon. Then, tell about some things you can do to help relieve stress. After each coping method, release some air from the balloon. Talk about how stress can be like this.

2. Interview people in particularly stressful jobs and ask them how they manage their stress. For example, seek out people who are in one of the following careers: police, medical professional, principal, teacher, counselor, coach, social worker, air traffic controller, or postal worker.

3. Write down one or more things that are causing you the most stress. Then attach the list to a helium balloon and release it. Or make a small "coffin" and have a stress funeral.

©YouthLight, Inc.

LESSON 10: ALCOHOL

"Alcohol may seem innocent. But it is responsible for the deaths of more people in the world than any other chemical we have ever known."
Anonymous

The lesson to be learned from the abuse of alcohol is a tragic and continuing one. Using alcohol may seem like fun at first. But, there is always a price that must be paid for drug use and this price can sometimes be fatal.

©YouthLight, Inc.

Larry's Story

Larry was a 10th grader who received high grades in school. The day before Memorial Day weekend, Larry was asked by friends to go to a party. They told him that several of his friends would be there.

At the party, there were many people who were drinking alcohol. Some of Larry's friends talked him into playing a drinking game. They gave him a half-pint of 150 proof rum and asked if he could drink it down without stopping. As he drank it, others cheered him on. The next day, a newspaper article reported that Larry had died. The doctor said he died from acute alcohol toxicity.

Larry and his friends appeared to be very smart in school. They each did well with their school work. But he and the others at the party weren't very intelligent about the drinking of alcohol. Peer pressure, ignorance about consumption of high-proof alcohol and poor judgement caused Larry's death.

Discussion Questions:

1. What do you believe were the main reasons that people at the party wanted Larry to drink the rum?

2. Why do you think Larry agreed to play the drinking game?

3. If you were at the party, what could you have done to help, before Larry started to drink the rum? While he was drinking it? After he drank it?

© YouthLight, Inc.

Reasons Teens Give for Drinking Alcohol

The following are reasons why some teens say they drink alcohol. Check the ones you feel are the actual reasons why they drink.

❑ They are curious about what will happen.

❑ There's nothing else they can think of to do.

❑ It looks cool on TV or in the movies.

❑ They want to feel accepted by others.

❑ They want to forget their problems.

❑ It helps them to socialize.

❑ They like how it tastes.

❑ It quenches their thirst.

❑ Their parents drink.

❑ Their friends drink.

❑ To act grown up.

❑ It is hereditary.

❑ It helps them relax.

❑ They want to have fun.

❑ They want to live dangerously.

❑ They think it will make them "cool."

❑ Because of commercials about alcohol.

❑ They are rebelling against their parents.

❑ They want to attract someone they like.

©YouthLight, Inc.

Reasons for Not Drinking Alcohol

The following are reasons that teens your age should not drink alcohol. Check the ones that you feel are the best reasons.

- ❏ It can make you throw up.

- ❏ You may end up doing things that you regret.

- ❏ It is illegal and you may get caught.

- ❏ It can cause you problems at school and at home.

- ❏ It can result in a terrible hangover.

- ❏ It can keep you from having fun in other ways.

- ❏ Drinking too much alcohol can kill you.

- ❏ It can make you even more angry or very sad.

- ❏ It can cause you to not care about yourself.

- ❏ You can end up in a dangerous situation.

- ❏ It is addictive and can be difficult to quit.

- ❏ Sooner or later, it can kill you.

- ❏ It can hurt your relationships with people in your family.

- ❏ You can lose respect from others your age.

- ❏ You can be taken advantage of in different ways.

- ❏ It can make you lazy.

- ❏ When you have a job, it can cause you to be fired.

- ❏ It makes you act like somebody that you are not.

©YouthLight, Inc.

Facts about Drinking Alcohol

Test your knowledge about alcohol and other drugs on the following statements. Write a "T" or "F" in the space before each item to indicate whether you believe the statement is true or false. Then, compare your answers to those on the next page.

_____ 1. Wine coolers have less alcohol than beer.

_____ 2. You can become addicted to beer.

_____ 3. Alcohol can increase someone's sex drive.

_____ 4. Alcohol use is one of the primary factors in the deaths of teenagers.

_____ 5. Teens say that their number one reason for drinking is because their friends do.

_____ 6. Drinking alcohol is not as bad as doing drugs.

_____ 7. Girls are slightly more affected by alcohol than boys.

_____ 8. Alcohol is currently the second biggest drug abuse problem among teens.

_____ 9. If someone is drunk and passes out, others should make sure the person is laying on his/her back.

_____ 10. You can inherit from your parents a tendency to become an alcoholic.

_____ 11. If a pregnant girl drinks only three beers, it won't cause severe birth defects in her unborn child.

_____ 12. Having only one beer won't hurt your ability to drive.

_____ 13. Excessive use of alcohol can damage your liver and lead to a deadly liver disease.

_____ 14. Most teens in the U.S. do not try alcohol for the first time until after they are 15 years old.

_____ 15. Most drowning victims have been drinking.

© YouthLight, Inc.

Answers

1. (False) Wine coolers typically contain 6% alcohol, while beer usually has 4% alcohol.

2. (True) Drinking beer excessively can lead to alcoholism.

3. (False) Alcohol does not increase sex drive. In fact, it reduces one's desire for and ability to have sex.

4. (True) Most deaths of teenagers have been related to drinking alcohol, whether these deaths are car accidents, falling, or other causes.

5. (True) According to one survey, seventy percent of teenagers say that their main reason for drinking is the influence of friends.

6. (False) Alcohol is a drug and is responsible for more deaths than the use of other drugs in the United States.

7. (True) In their digestive systems, females have lower amounts of an enzyme that breaks down some of the alcohol before it enters the bloodstream.

8. (False) Alcohol is currently the most significant substance abuse problem among adolescents.

9. (False) If someone passes out on their back, they should be rolled over on their side. Too many people have died from breathing their own vomit into their lungs. This is how Jimmy Hendrix, the famous rock guitar player, died.

10. (True) Alcoholism has been shown to have a genetic factor.

11. (False) While this may not harm the child, then again, it may. Fetal alcohol syndrome is caused by the mother drinking alcohol while she's pregnant. The exact amount of alcohol it takes to harm the unborn child is unknown.

12. (False) Any amount of alcohol will slow your ability to make judgments and react. If you drive, don't drink! If you drink, don't drive!

13. (True) Your liver primarily serves to neutralize, or detoxify any chemicals in the body that it identifies as poisonous. Alcohol is one of these chemicals. Excessive drinking over a long period of time eventually will lead to a deadly disease called cirrhosis of the liver. Some alcoholics, even knowing that their livers are diseased, continue to drink until they die.

14. (False) In one survey, more than 60% of 15 year-olds report that they have consumed alcohol in the past.

15. (True) Of all drowning victims in the U.S., about 70% had been drinking alcohol at the time.

©YouthLight, Inc.

LESSON 11: OTHER DRUGS

"Drugs lie! They promise you happiness, and then they let you down."

Anonymous

Alcohol and other drugs are being used by an increasing number of young people. Some students begin using drugs when they are in elementary school. Using a drug is never worth the risks involved. Drugs may seem like fun at first, but one day an unexpected problem will strike. Whether it's becoming ill, getting busted and going to jail, losing a boy or girlfriend, getting fired from a good job, being robbed or assaulted, becoming hospitalized, or dying, the eventual results of drug use are always bad and never worth taking the risk that they won't result in tragedy.

© YouthLight, Inc.

Lisa's Story

Lisa was a ninth grader who spent most of her time after school with three close friends. One day two boys walked up to Lisa and her friends and started talking with them. Lisa was very attracted to one of the boys, but tried not to let him know.

Soon, the boy who Lisa thought was good looking took out of his pocket a bag containing what looked like a drug. He asked the girls if they wanted to try it. Lisa said "no" at first, but one of her friends said that she had done this kind of drug plenty of times before and that is was "cool." Strangely, this girl did not want to do the drug this time, but persuaded Lisa to try it.

The boy gave Lisa the drug. At first, Lisa felt a little dizzy. Soon, her heart started beating very fast and she began breathing quickly. But the boys told her not to worry and said that this effect was expected. Then Lisa suddenly passed out on the ground. One boy asked the other, "Where did you get that stuff?" The other boy answered, "I found it in my brother's drawer at home." Both boys looked at each other, then they took off running, leaving Lisa's "friends" to figure out what to do next.

Discussion Questions:

1. What do you believe are the reasons that Lisa tried the drug?

2. Why did one of her friends say that she had already tried the drug and that it was "cool"? Do you believe she had actually tried it before? If not, why would she lie?

3. What do you think the so-called "drug" might really have been?

4. What should her friends have done before Lisa took the drug? What should they have done after Lisa passed out?

5. What do you think should happen to the two boys?

©YouthLight, Inc.

Observations of Drug Use

Check which of the following statements are true.

❑ I have seen someone intoxicated or stoned on a drug other than alcohol.
❑ I have been offered drugs by someone.
❑ I know someone who has a problem with drugs.
❑ I know where I could get drugs.
❑ I have used one or more drugs in the past.
❑ I have seen someone use:

❑ Marijuana   ❑ Heroin
❑ Alcohol   ❑ 'Shrooms (psychedelic mushrooms)
❑ Caffeine   ❑ Angel Dust (PCP)
❑ Tobacco   ❑ Downers (barbiturates/tranquilizers)
❑ LSD   ❑ Steroids (for body building)
❑ Cocaine   ❑ Inhalants (like gasoline or glue)
❑ Speed   ❑ Other drugs:
❑ Ecstasy   _____

Discussion Questions:

1   Which of these drugs are you unfamiliar with? Look them up in a book, or ask a counselor or nurse.

2. Which drug do you believe is the first one most kids experience before try others on the list?

3. Which three drugs on the list do you believe are the most dangerous?

4. Which three do you believe are the least dangerous? Talk about how these drugs are dangerous anyway.

5. Have you ever lost a friendship because of drugs?

6. Have you ever known someone who died, or almost died, while using drugs? What happened?

7. Have you ever known someone who committed a crime while intoxicated or high?

8. Have you ever known someone who needed help for their drug use, but did not get it?

©YouthLight, Inc.

Fun Without Drugs

Some adults believe that the main reason teens begin using drugs is because someone pushes them into it. However, interviews with young people indicate that the primary reason adolescents use drugs is because they believe that becoming intoxicated or high will be "fun." While having fun is an important part of life, there are many other ways to have fun that are much safer and don't make you sick afterwards.

If someone is going to promise never to use drugs, he/she will need to know many ways to have natural fun without the use of chemical intoxicants. Place a check mark in front of the following things you could enjoy doing without drugs.

❑ Play team sports such as baseball, basketball, soccer, football or hockey.

❑ Play any of the above sports without being on a formal team.

❑ Play games such as pool, chess, checkers, cards, video games or board games.

❑ Go bowling with some friends.

❑ Go skating or skate boarding with friends.

❑ Go snow skiing or sledding with friends.

❑ Go swimming or boating with friends.

❑ Learn to play a musical instrument.

❑ Listen to music alone or with friends.

❑ Go dancing.

❑ Write poetry, music, and/or lyrics.

❑ Create something with arts or crafts.

❑ Get involved in one or more interest clubs.

❑ Take up martial arts.

❑ Hang out only with friends who are drug free.

❑ Go to the shopping mall.

❑ Go camping or hiking.

❑ Plan a drug-free event in your neighborhood.

❑ Plan a trip with your friends.

❑ Go biking.

❑ Go to a local recreational facility.

❑ Go to drug/alcohol free parties.

❑ Take up a hobby such as collecting something.

❑ Watch television.

❑ Go to the movies.

❑ Learn to cook.

❑ Go watch a sport's team practice or play.

❑ Go to a park with some friends.

❑ Mentor a young child.

©YouthLight, Inc.

A Message to a Child

If you were going to talk with an eight year-old child about drugs, what are three things you would say?

1.

2.

3.

Optional Activities

1. Interview a drug rehabilitation counselor. Beforehand, work with your counselor to make a list of interview questions.

2. Talk with your school's DARE or Safety Officer, if you have one, about the drug problem.

3. Make a list of drug free groups and events in your community in which you can get involved.

4. Work with your counselor and perhaps with others in your program to organize a drug-free event in your school or community.

©YouthLight, Inc.

©YouthLight, Inc.

LESSON 12: ANGER MANAGEMENT

©YouthLight, Inc.

"(Anger) starts with madness and ends with regret."
Abraham Hasdai

Anger is a normal human emotion that we should not try to eliminate from our lives. However, if we do not understand why we become angry and how we can manage it, difficulties result.

Anger is sometimes called a "secondary" emotion because we usually experience feelings of hurt, frustration, loss, or fear before anger develops. Think about which of these emotions might come first before you become angry in different situations. Remember that different people become angry about different things.

Allison's Story

Allison almost always had an angry look on her face. She knew she became angry a lot, but really didn't know why. She had been that way ever since she could remember. Allison was determined to never let anyone disrespect her without "paying a price." Unfortunately, it was Allison who usually ended up paying the price for her anger.

One day Allison had finally reached her limit with a girl at school who she claimed was telling lies about her. Allison was in a rage. She was so mad that she didn't think clearly. At the beginning of her lunch period, Allison found the girl and started hitting her without saying a word. Before the end of the day, Allison was suspended once again. The principal warned her that if she continued her violent behavior, she would be expelled from school.

When she returned to school, Allison met with a counselor who helped her finally discover the source of her anger. When she was three years–old her mother had died. Allison had made herself forget about the pain and grief from this horrible event. Because she had never really talked about this situation with someone, it continued to affect her life. Underneath, Allison remained angry that her mother had "left" her when she died.

Once Allison realized why she became angry so often, her counselor encouraged her to begin exploring different strategies she could use to help her get over her mother's death and control her anger. Allison still became angry sometimes, but she eventually learned to manage it much better.

Discussion Questions:

1. Why do you believe so many young people use fighting as a way to express anger?

2. What else could Allison have done when she was angry at the girl, that would have had a better outcome?

3. What would you have done if you were in a similar situation?

4. When have you felt hurt, frustration, loss, or fear before your anger developed?

©YouthLight, Inc.

What Makes you Angry?

Use the following numbers to rate how angry or frustrated you become in each situation below. Then share your answers with your counselor.

1 = No problem   *3* = Frustrated   *4* = Very Angry

2 = A Little Frustrated   *5* = Extremely Angry

How angry do you become when someone:

Promises to do a favor for you, then forgets.	*1*	*2*	*3*	*4*	*5*
Ignores you.	*1*	*2*	*3*	*4*	*5*
Blames you for something you didn't do.	*1*	*2*	*3*	*4*	*5*
Yells at you for doing something wrong.	*1*	*2*	*3*	*4*	*5*
Threatens to hurt you.	*1*	*2*	*3*	*4*	*5*
Starts a bad rumor about you.	*1*	*2*	*3*	*4*	*5*
Steals from you.	*1*	*2*	*3*	*4*	*5*
Tells you a lie.	*1*	*2*	*3*	*4*	*5*
Tells a lie about you.	*1*	*2*	*3*	*4*	*5*

Other *(List other situations that make you angry and rate yourself on each.)*

_____   *1*   *2*   *3*   *4*   *5*

_____   *1*   *2*   *3*   *4*   *5*

_____   *1*   *2*   *3*   *4*   *5*

©YouthLight, Inc.

Anger Control

The following lists provide some ideas for preventing or handling anger in positive and negative ways.

Directions: Check which of the following "Helpful" and "Unhelpful" ideas you use to control your anger. Then, discuss which of these ideas would be most appropriate for each situation from the previous page in "What Makes You Angry."

Helpful Ideas

❑ Talk it out with someone

❑ Count to "10"

❑ Take a deep breath

❑ Find a place to be alone

❑ Listen to music

❑ Punch a pillow

❑ Clean or organize your room

❑ Scream

❑ Walk, jog, or run

❑ Write it out

❑ Talk to yourself

❑ Play with clay or Play Doh®

❑ Draw your feelings

❑ Watch TV

❑ Go Shopping

❑ Play a sport

Unhelpful Ideas

❑ Eat a lot more (or less)

❑ Drive fast

❑ Use drugs/alcohol/inhalants

❑ Fight

❑ Threaten to hurt someone

❑ Hurt yourself

❑ Withdraw from everyone

❑ Blame it on someone else

❑ Take it out on an animal

❑ Destroy property

❑ Start a rumor

❑ Run away from home

❑ Skip class or school

❑ Laugh at the person

❑ Yell, cuss at the person

❑ Give an obscene gesture

©YouthLight, Inc.

Optional Activities

1. Look through a magazine or newspaper for examples of people who were angry. How did they deal with their anger? What was the outcome?

2. Interview people in highly stressful jobs who have to deal with their anger. Ask them what they do to control their anger.

3. Visit a juvenile detention center.

4. Discuss the meaning of the following: "Anger is like a bomb. . .to make it safe, disarm its fuse."

©YouthLight, Inc.

©YouthLight, Inc.

LESSON 13: CONFLICT RESOLUTION

"You cannot shake hands with a clenched fist."
Indira Gandhi

Having conflicts with others is an inevitable part of life. Unless you choose to live the remainder of your life as a hermit, you will have to face occasional disputes with other people. Our successes or failures in handling these disputes depend in part on our mastery of skills and techniques of conflict resolution.

©YouthLight, Inc.

The Feud

Kelly and Tonya hated each other. But it wasn't always that way. When they were younger, the two girls were best friends. Then, during their eighth grade year, Tonya accused Kelly of "stealing" her boyfriend away from her. Years later, they continued to make little negative comments whenever they were around each other. A few times, these little comments caused one or the other girl to lose her temper and start fighting.

This year, each girl developed a group of her own supporters who would help spread rumors about the other girl. Eventually, some of these "friends" from each group began to threaten each other. Recently, even the girls' mothers have become upset at one another.

Kelly and Tonya spent a lot of their teenage years being upset at each other. They were the ultimate victims of this feud. Each of the girls suffered from negative rumors, stayed awake at night with anger and bitterness, and were eventually suspended from school for fighting.

Kelly's and Tonya's conflict was unfortunate. First, they probably could have resolved it long ago. Second, the conflict eventually took far too much of a toll on these girls, their friends, and their families. This entire situation should have been handled much differently by everyone involved. Discuss some ways the conflict might have been handled better.

Discussion Questions:

1. Have you ever experienced a feud with someone? How did it start? How did it end?

2. Why do you believe other people become involved so easily in a conflict between two people?

3. How could Kelly and Tonya have worked out their differences before the situation became out of control? What could they have done to help work things out later, after they were suspended from school?

4. What could the girls' friends do to help them work out their feud at this point in time?

5. Do you believe there are some conflicts in which fighting is the only way to work things out? Why or why not?

©YouthLight, Inc.

Handling Conflicts

There are many ways that people try to resolve conflicts. What are some of the advantages and disadvantages of the following ways?

- Yelling
- Ignoring
- Fighting
- Laughing at the person
- Talking about it with a friend
- Trying to forget about it
- Talking about it with a teacher, counselor, or parent
- Writing a letter to the person
- Spreading a rumor about the person
- Asking some friends to help you get revenge
- Trying to "talk it out" with the person in private
- Trying to "talk it out" with the person, in the presence of others

When you have conflicts with other people, how do you handle them? Discuss how you would probably handle the following situations:

- If someone cut in line in front of you.

- If your parent (guardian) told you that you couldn't do something you really wanted to do.

- If you found that one of your friends has been telling lies about you.

- If your teacher became upset with you in class.

- If someone threatened to fight you.

- If someone accused you of doing something that you didn't do.

© YouthLight, Inc.

Four-Step
Conflict Resolution Model

Sometimes, it seems like there are no good ways to resolve a conflict. When this happens, you will have to do the best you can in the situation. The following Conflict Resolution Model can help you make wiser decisions about how to handle your conflicts with others. It will provide you with a method that you can use with your parent(s), teachers, and others your age. You may also find that it can be used to help others work through some of their conflicts.

To build your skills in using this model, you may want to try out each step by role-playing some practice situations with a friend or your counselor. As you master the steps and learn how to apply them to a variety of situations, you will acquire some powerful tools to help you handle conflicts wisely.

Step 1: "What is the conflict about?"
Consider how the conflict started and try to think about both sides of the conflict as much as possible.

Step 2: "What approaches have you tried?"
Make a written list of all the approaches you've tried so far to resolve this conflict. After each item, write what happened as a result.

Step 3: "What else could you do?
Continue your list of approaches by adding any new ideas you may have to resolve this conflict. As in "Step 2", write what you believe will be the probable outcome or result of each strategy. If you cannot think of any new approaches, explore what would probably happen if you did nothing.

Step 4: "What's your first step?"
Look through your list of approaches and outcomes from Steps 2 and 3 and pick the one you will start with. Remember, if you decide to do none of the approaches, you still have made a choice that will have its own result. Commit to a day and time you will do this "first step." Then take action! Later, you may want to look back at your list to consider other ideas, in case the first step doesn't resolve the situation.

©YouthLight, Inc.

Optional Activities

1. Interview a professional mediator. You can find a list of these professionals in the Yellow Pages of your phone directory under a term similar to "Mediation Services," or contact your local courthouse for information.

2. Find out if your school or community has a peer mediation and/or a student court program. Volunteer to become involved in one of these programs.

3. Fill a small pan or plastic container half full of cornstarch paste. This is made by adding water to cornstarch powder slowly until a very thick paste results. Then place your fingers in the paste. You will notice that when you push hard against the paste, it will resist and feel like a solid. But, when you ease your fingers into the paste, the resistance disappears, allowing easy dipping. The point is that when attempting to resolve a personal conflict, a hurried, forceful approach usually causes resistance. On the other hand, a gentle, easy, and patient approach to conflict resolution will more likely result in discovering and working out the underlying issues.

© YouthLight, Inc.

©YouthLight, Inc.

LESSON 14: BEING ASSERTIVE

"One of the most important tasks teenagers have is to slowly and deliberately learn how to take charge of their own lives."

Anonymous

All of us become upset at times with things that others say or do. How we respond in these situations will tell others something about us. We don't want to respond too strongly or too weakly. When people upset us, we should try to be assertive. This means that we should be able to respectfully tell others about something they said or did that bothered us. When this happens, the statement we make to them is called a confrontation. All of us face, from time to time, situations in which we must confront others.

© YouthLight, Inc.

Nathan and Derek's Story

Nathan and Derek had many similar interests, but there was one primary difference between them. When Nathan felt the least bit upset about something, everyone around him soon knew about it. He was determined to stand up for himself and frequently confronted others in a very aggressive way. Nathan believed in being open and honest with his feelings. However, others sometimes avoided him because they felt he was insensitive and self-centered. They saw him as "too aggressive."

Derek, on the other hand, was shy and reserved. When he was upset at someone, he usually became quiet and walked away. He usually kept his true feelings hidden from others and rarely would confront someone. Derek believed in being very careful not to upset people's feelings. Because of Derek's nature, other students sometimes took advantage of him because they felt he was weak and wouldn't stand up to other people. They saw him as "too passive."

As a result of Nathan's aggressive style or Derek's passive nature, each boy had frequent problems with other students. They both would improve their relationships with others by learning how to be more assertive.

When confronting others, some people are too aggressive. This means that they are overly critical and harsh to others when they are upset. People eventually learn to avoid aggressive people because they don't like being treated so negatively.

Some people are too passive. This means they often avoid sharing their feelings when they are bothered by others. Passive people are sometimes taken advantage of and picked on by others.

Assertive people have a style that is between aggressive and passive. This is usually the most effective way to handle yourself when you need to confront others.

Discussion Questions:

1. Who do you know that is too passive? Too aggressive? What are the results of their styles of confrontation?

2. Who do you know that handles him/herself well when confronting others? When have you heard this person being assertive to someone?

3. Which style are you closest to: passive, assertive, or aggressive? What do you believe you need to work on to improve your ability to be more assertive?

©YouthLight, Inc.

Passive, Assertive, or Aggressive?

In the blanks that appear in front of the items listed below, use numbers 1, 2, or 3 to indicate whether this result would most likely be experienced by a student who is too passive, assertive, or too aggressive. Note that the answers are printed upside down at the bottom of this page.

1 = Too Passive (Usually trying to avoid expressing their feelings)

2 = Assertive (Carefully wording expressions of their feelings)

3 = Too Aggressive (Usually telling others in a strong, direct manner about their feelings, without trying to be tactful)

The student who is most likely to be:

_____ Suspended from school for fighting.

_____ Thought of as a "weak" person.

_____ Respected by others.

_____ Thought of as a rude person.

_____ Thought of as an effective leader.

_____ Picked on by others.

_____ Thought of as a strong, but caring person.

_____ Becoming ill someday, because of held-in feelings.

_____ Abusive to others.

Passive people need to build their confidence so they can confront others when needed. Aggressive people should practice being more sensitive to other's feelings when they become upset.

Good leaders have effective confrontation skills. They are not too harsh or too weak when they tell others how they feel. By practicing effective confrontations, you will learn an important leadership skill that will help you relate better with others throughout your life.

Answers: (1) 3; (2) 1; (3) 2; (4) 3; (5) 2; (6) 1; (7) 2; (8) 1; (9) 3.

©YouthLight, Inc.

Tips for Confronting Others

Remember, when deciding how to confront someone:

- **Choose your battles carefully.** That is, don't confront people each time you feel a little upset. Pick wisely which times you should confront a person, and which times you should let the situation pass by without saying anything.

- **Watch your timing.** It is sometimes best not to confront someone when you are very upset. Take some time to cool down and find the best words to say before you confront them

- **Use the "Three Step Confrontation Model."** This model can be helpful in planning how to give an effective confrontation (see next page).

- **Be prepared to be a good listener.** After giving your confrontation, you will need to listen carefully as the other person responds. Then, if you think that the person did not clearly understand what you were saying, tell the confrontation again.

©YouthLight, Inc.

Three Step Confrontation Model

This model will help you construct the most effective assertive statement you can give to others. When confronting others, try to use all three steps in any order.

Step 1: *Tell the person specifically what he/she said or did.*

Step 2: *Tell the feeling you are experiencing.*

Step 3: *Explain how this feeling has affected you.*

The following is an example of a confrontation using the three steps of the Confrontation Model. Look for each of the three steps in this statement.

> "I heard you telling Heather that I went out with her boyfriend. It made me mad because it's not true. I thought you were my friend, but now I'm not sure I can trust you."

On the lines that follow, write your own three step confrontation to someone who has said or done something that has upset you.

_____

_____

_____

_____

_____

_____

Optional Activities

1. Look for/or join a martial arts training program that features violence prevention and personal growth.

2. Practice role-playing situations you actually are facing.

© YouthLight, Inc.

©YouthLight, Inc.

LESSON 15: RACISM

"Racism will use any excuse to excuse itself."
Mary McLeod Bethune

Racism, like other forms of prejudice, is a prejudgment about someone based on a limited number of facts. For example, many people have experienced someone judging them based on, as Martin Luther King said, "the color of their skin, rather than on the content of their character."

© YouthLight, Inc.

Bessie Coleman's Story *

Ever since Bessie Coleman was a little girl, she dreamed of being a pilot. It was the early part of the 1900s and airplanes were a rare sight to behold.

In Bessie's childhood, life was not easy. She had to pick cotton to help support her family. When Bessie was in her 20's, she decided she was going to reach her dream of learning how to fly an airplane. She tried very hard to find a flight school that would give her lessons and she was turned down by every flight instructor she approached. Most of them were appalled that a woman would want to fly, especially a black woman! There were no African American pilots at that time.

After many failed attempts, Bessie finally found a flight school in France that would accept her. She worked hard at several jobs to earn the money for the trip and attended a "language school" to learn French. Then, she made her way to Europe. There she was licensed as a pilot, two years before Amelia Earhart had received her pilot license. After returning from France, Bessie became a stunt flyer and traveled across the United States.

Bessie Coleman was the first African American to earn an international pilot's license and the first black woman in the world to fly an airplane. Known later as "Queen Bess" she challenged racism and bigotry to reach her dream.

Though Bessie Coleman experienced racism in her quest to reach her dream, she did not let that get in her way. Like Bessie, many of us have experienced racism, or other forms of prejudice, and have overcome it. It would be best if no racism existed, but unfortunately, it does.

Discussion Questions:

1. How much racism do you believe is in your school? In your community?

2. What programs are in your school and/or community to help combat racism?

3. How might Bessie Coleman's life been different had she let racism discourage her from becoming a pilot?

4. When have you or someone you know experienced racism?

* Adapted from Rich (1993)

©YouthLight, Inc.

Experiences With Racism

Check the items in the list below, if you have ever experienced any of these situations involving racism. Discuss each situation, how you felt, and what you did about it.

I have been:

❑ Teased or laughed at.
❑ Discouraged from trying to do something.
❑ Talked about behind my back.
❑ Treated overly nice, without sincerity.
❑ Forbidden from going somewhere (or with someone).
❑ Denied admission into a club or other group.

❑ Ignored.
❑ Threatened.
❑ Held back from opportunities.
❑ Blamed for something that happened.

Origins of Racism

How do people develop racism? Check any items below that you believe are the origins of racism in people. Discuss which items you believe are the biggest causes of racism and why.

❑ Birth (genetic)
❑ Parent's beliefs
❑ Negative past experiences
❑ Fears
❑ Jealousy
❑ Organized groups
❑ Friends' beliefs

❑ Not being around people of other cultures
❑ Things that happened in past history
❑ Outspoken leaders
❑ Poverty
❑ Ignorance
❑ Media such as movies, television, and music
❑ Other _____

© YouthLight, Inc.

Doing Something About Racism

What can you do to help prevent or reduce racism? Look through the following list and check what you have done in your school and/or community. Then, place a star next to any item you would consider doing sometime during the next year.

___ Construct a bulletin board on "Cultural Unity."

___ Become a friend to someone of a different culture from you.

___ Start a multicultural study group.

___ Confront someone when they tell a racial joke.

___ Organize a multicultural event at your school.

___ Become a mentor to a child who is a different culture from you.

___ Reach out to a new student who is a different culture from you.

___ Write an article for your school newspaper on cultural diversity.

___ Organize a one-day conference for students on cultural unity.

___ Develop a multicultural theme skit or play for younger students.

Optional Activities

1. Go to the school media center or to a library and look up information about famous people who overcame or worked to reduce racism.

2. Look through magazines and/or newspapers and find examples of racial issues.

3. William A. Ward once said prejudice was, "A disease characterized by hardening of the categories." Discuss the meaning of this statement.

©YouthLight, Inc.

References

Bowman, R.P. (1997). *Study With a Buddy*. Chapin, SC: YouthLight, Inc. (In development).

Josephson Institute of Ethics (Dec., 1992). *Developing Moral Values in Youth. Ethics: Easier Said Than Done.* (Marina Del Rey, CA), Issues 19&20, 80-81.

Klots, S. (1995). *Carl Lewis Story*. New York: Chelsea House Publishers

Mosley, L.(1976). *Charles Lindbergh*. Garden City, New York: Doubleday.

Rich, D.L. (1993). *Queen Bess: Daredevil Aviator*. Washington, D.C.: Smithsonian Institute Press.